TWELVE TALES OF THE LIFE
AND ADVENTURES OF SAINT IMAGINUS

TWELVE TALES OF THE LIFE
AND ADVENTURES
OF SAINT IMAGINUS

*Retold from the Collection made by his Brethren
of the Order of Saint Simplicitas, with additional
stories now published for the first time*

Edited by

FRANCES MARGARET McGUIRE

With illustrations by
BETTY ARNOTT

NEW YORK

SHEED & WARD

1947

MANUFACTURED IN THE UNITED STATES OF AMERICA
BY THE HADDON CRAFTSMEN, INC.
SCRANTON, PA.

CONTENTS

FOREWORD

Little is known of the early life of Saint Imaginus. He seems to have been born of good, though respectable, parents and to have spent his boyhood in the country.

In a Manuscript included in the "Memoria" of Liebluyt, recently translated and edited by Dom Nullus Nemoque, O.S.S., there is told how one Imaginus, while teaching some boys to play hop-scotch outside the Monastery of Saint Aegrid, was chased by the porter; and how he reproved the porter, saying, "Beware, Brother Porter, lest in chasing away these boys from the gate of the Monastery, you let the monks escape." Whereupon the Lay Brother took him back to the gate and gave him some honey to eat. Dom Nullus contends that this was the youthful Imaginus of the "Wondrous Life," putting forward the argument that not only was Saint Aegrid's the very monastic house in which Imaginus is known to have spent his novitiate, but that the story also indicates his powers of prophecy, meaning that his reproval of the porter shows that he already knew of his vocation and that the "monks" who might escape were in reality himself and his companions.

This, however, is difficult to reconcile with the fact, well established by the researches of Riotto, Itzbaum and others (vide Proc. Hagi. Socy. Series ccclv., tome MCCIX) that at the date of this story Imaginus was already ordained priest and a man of some thirty years of age. There is always the possibility that his sanctity bestowed on him the power of translating himself through time as other saints have had the power of miraculous bilocation (notably Blessed Martin Porres and Saint Joseph of Cupertino). Nor is the present Editor sceptical of such a possibility. It would serve to explain many of the discrepancies in the tales which have come down to us of the circumstances and events of his life.

The stories in the collection which follows are largely taken from that made by Merritsz of Amsterdam, who published them in both Latin and Dutch. ("Descriptio ac delineatio ecclesiastica detectionis freti sunt, Transitus ad Occasum super tractu recens detecto, in quinta Orbis parte, cui nomen Australia incognita"; Amsterodami: Ex officina Heffilij Merardi.)

Three years after the Merritsz publication, an English edition of the same work appeared under the title: "A Defcription of the Wondrous Life and Works of Saint Imaginus, Servant of God and ordained Prieft of the Order of Ste. Simplicitas; and of the difcoveries, Acts and Occurrents, miraculous and otherwife, of his life, his travailes and admirable adventures in the Fifth part of the World recently difcovered, wherein he did meet with divers strange perfons and manifold chances. Printed by Guillaume Sharply at his bookshop in Saint Ethylfingers Court for private circulation."

Two stories in the present collection were not included in these earlier editions and now appear in English for the first time. The first of these, "The Story of the Bishop's Pie," was found pasted to the inside of a parchment folio in the Library at Bonn. The second, "The

FOREWORD

Story of the Obstinate Cow," was told to the present Editor by someone who had it from an ancient man who had it from those who remembered the incidents therein described.

1. THE STORY OF THE WICKED YOUNG MEN

It so happened and befell that soon after Imaginus had arrived at the town wherein he was to begin his pastoral labours (for it will be understood that the monks of this country were not able to observe the full seclusion of monastic life, owing to the necessity of teaching among the heathen of the place), he was walking along the street when he was attacked by a party of ruffianly young men who set upon him and beat him unmercifully. In vain he tried to bear their blows in patience while speaking to them peaceably. They did but cry out the louder and beat him the harder so that he was at last obliged to take his departure as best he could. Whereupon they pursued him with stones and flints which they picked up from the roadside (where they lay in abundance) and threw after him. Nor could he fail to be struck by the accuracy with which they aimed these missiles at his person.

Seeing him sore perplexed, the Parish Priest asked him the reason, and Imaginus (though in no spirit of complaint but rather from obedience) told him all that had befallen, and added that it would be as well if these same young men could be converted to a life of good order and the practice of Christian virtue. The Parish Priest agreed that this would indeed be well, but added:

"You are young and zealous, Father Imaginus, and so have hope to spare for such things. For my part, I have worked in this same parish for three-and-twenty years and during all that time there have been unruly and scoundrelly young men who would set upon any priest they met, so that I have long since abandoned any idea of their conversion." So saying he gave Father Imaginus a pot of ointment and went out.

But Imaginus continued to perplex himself, putting the jar of ointment on one side that he might dedicate the pain of his injuries the more readily to the salvation of the villains who had so misused him. Nor, as long as the pain lasted, could he forbear to ponder on the matter, turning over in his mind ways by which he could bring these wicked young men to a knowledge and love of truth. So often and at such length did he speak of it that at last the patience of his superior was exhausted, and he forbade him to broach the subject further, "for, look you, Father Imaginus," he said, "it says in the Scriptures that the cockle shall be left among the wheat till the harvest when the good shall be sifted from the bad and the bad cast into the fire."

So Imaginus forbore to speak of it again, out of respect for his Superior, other than to say, "In the Scriptures it is also said that he who stole let him now steal no more; but rather let him labour, working with his hands the thing which is good, that he may have something to give to him that suffereth need."

He did not himself understand why these words came so readily to his lips, but, continuing to turn them over in his mind, he perceived that they contained a wisdom by which he was surely meant to profit. Going therefore to the open ground behind the presbytery, he picked up a number of stones and began to cast them at a small tree which grew there. And this he did every day for several days.

The Parish Priest, seeing him, thought that he meditated revenge against the young men who had beaten him, and reproved him, saying, "I myself have given one of these young men a straight left on the jaw. But this was when I was younger. It is true that they no longer molest me, but it is also true that I have not brought them to a knowledge of the True Faith. So be not tempted to raise your hand against them." And Imaginus receiving his counsel, agreed that it was wise. Nevertheless, he continued to throw stones at the little tree and every day grew more sure of his aim so that seldom did he fail to strike it. And he studied diligently at certain books and every day became more silent so that the Parish Priest looked at him with wonder, fearing for his sanity.

And it so happened and befell, that Imaginus was walking along the road after visiting a sick person (for he was assiduous in the pursuit of his pastoral duties) when he once again met the wicked young men who had attacked him. Who, when they saw that it was Imaginus approaching, at once took up stones to cast at him. But he said to them, "You aim very badly and your stones have no spin. You should throw like this." And, reaching down, he picked up a number of stones (saying at the same time within himself, "Dextera tua, Domine, glorificata est in virtute," and calling on the intercession of Saint Stephen), he threw the stones one at a time at a small tree which grew beside the road a great distance away, and he hit the small tree with each stone.

Then the young men contended that they also could hit the tree and they threw stones but could not hit it because of its great distance. Then Imaginus took up a stout stave which lay near at hand and the young men thought he intended to beat them with it. Standing in front of the tree he invited them to throw stones at him. Greatly astonished, they did so and he hit the stones with the piece of wood so that they flew into the air and were lost. Then he gave the stave to one of the young men who found that he could not hit the stones, and Imaginus showed him how.

The next day they returned to the same place, Imaginus bringing with him a wooden bat and a ball of hard rubber, explaining that they would use these instead of the stones and the stave of wood.

He showed them how the bat could be used to prevent the ball from hitting the tree, and if by chance the ball did hit the tree the bat was taken away from that player and given to another. He showed them also how the ball could be thrown in such manner as to hit the tree in spite of the bat, or if the ball were hit by the bat it could be caught before it had gone very far.

After they had played like this for several days, Imaginus counted the number of the young men and they were five. So he told them to bring six other young men on the following day and they would play in a field nearby with two bats and some staves of wood stuck into the ground instead of the little tree. And so interested were they that two groups were formed each of eleven and they took turns in wielding the bats and chasing the balls.

Now the Parish Priest happening to notice that Imaginus healed him of his wounds without acquiring fresh ones, he thought to ask him if he had met the wicked young men again.

"Why, yes, I have met them often," was his reply.

"Did they not attack you again?" asked the Priest.

"They did attack me, father," said Imaginus, "but the man who would have peace himself sets his enemies to fighting each other." Whereupon his Superior was very angry and said that if he had done this it was a grave sin. And Imaginus bore the rebuke silently, feeling that he deserved it for his levity. And he took the Parish Priest to the field where the young men were playing and when he saw them the Parish Priest could not contain his astonishment, and he said to Father Imaginus, "We will have a cricket match and take up a collection for the church debt."

Then he said that he wished to compliment him on his success in turning them from their evil ways; but Imaginus, in his humility, would not accept the praise, and taking a book from his pocket, he said "I learnt it from Grace."

2. THE STORY OF THE PERPLEXED ANGEL

If you would understand the story I am about to relate, you must know that Saint Imaginus had a great friendship with the angel guardians of men. He not only talked with his own guardian angel (whose name was Prudentia) but with the guardians of other men. He loved to gather the pure spirits round him and to converse with them of heavenly things. Especially was he accustomed to speak with the Azurii or guardian angels of the souls in Purgatory. Many of these suffering souls had been his parishioners and it was but natural that he should be interested in their spiritual progress. He gave their guardian angels much good counsel concerning them.

It is recorded that, on one occasion, he was visiting the city of Melbourne, and suffered there from the way the guardian angels were kept busy caring for the bodies of their charges, so that there was but little time left for the care of souls. All day, and at night too, the angels were occupied with helping their charges across the streets, warning them of swift-moving vehicles and drawing their attention to traffic lights and the signals of policemen. The drivers of the vehicles, too, required much care and had it not been for the constant and powerful co-operation of Saint Christopher, it is doubtful whether the guardian angels could have coped with the burden of their duties.

What was the dismay of Saint Imaginus therefore to discover that there was yet another occupation

7

demanded of the spirits: one, certainly, which they could exercise in their own element. I speak of the guardianship of aviators. This brought him to the problem of the Perplexed Angel.

How it came about was in this wise:

The Parish Priest of the place in which Imaginus was exercising his curacy was invited by his parishioners to a display of aerobatics which was to take place at an open space some distance from the city. The daughter of the good parishioner who extended the invitation was betrothed to a young aviator who was to take part in the display. It came about that, after promising to be present, the Parish Priest was prevented from attending, and in order that no discourtesy might seem to extend to his prospective host, he instructed Imaginus to take his place. Happy in the performance of his obedience, Imaginus betook himself to the scene of the festivities. Here there was a great field with many aeroplanes in the centre and a vast assemblage of people round the edge.

Imaginus found his host and hostess and their family. They had spread rugs and cushions on the grass (which was green at that time of the year) and put out many rich and varied viands, with vessels of wine and tea and other refreshments. Imaginus, who usually observed the rules of abstinence, ate and drank liberally out of courtesy to his host and also not to seem lacking in playing the part assigned to him by his Parish Priest.

While he was eating, the daughter of his host brought her betrothed to be introduced to the good father. What was Imaginus's dismay when he found the young

man surrounded by a dark haze which denoted his
infidelity. It was with the greatest difficulty that the
Saint was able to respond to his greeting, so stricken
was he by the unhappy destiny which must await the
young man and his bride. He made haste to take up
the matter with the guardian angel, whom he found to
be named Zestia. This poor spirit was in a sad plight
indeed. Worn quite thin with the effort required to keep
her charge from falling into deeper sin, her face was
pale and sad, and her wings drooping and even moulting.
"It is the flying," she wept when Imaginus gently
questioned her. "I fear so much that he will crash
while in the state of infidelity that at times I carry
the whole weight of the aeroplane on my own wings.
If only he wouldn't spin dive!"

Imaginus looked at the young man and saw that he
was suffering from a certain vanity not uncommon
in young men of his age and station. This had led him
to rank his own wisdom higher than that of Revealed
Truth.

Imaginus and his own guardian angel, Prudentia,
did what they could to cheer and sustain Zestia but,
while grateful for their kindness, she could not be raised
in spirits. "It's this afternoon," she explained. "Today
it will be worse than usual. They are going to do mass
formation flying. There was one moment last night
when he thought of going to Confession. I gave him a
terrible picture of hell, but he threw it away saying that
he had more sense than to be scared by a child's story.
Perhaps I have used the wrong tactics with him. But
I was so hoping that he would bale out at the last minute

and make a safe landing." She looked at Father Imaginus timidly.

"Be of good courage, child," he said to her. "Do your best to help him this afternoon and I will be waiting for you."

She did not understand what he meant by this, for unlike the saints, angels are not able to see into the future. But Imaginus could see a little way and he prayed that by the mercy of the Divine Power he could help the perplexed angel and save the soul of the young aviator. Calling to Prudentia, he therefore took up his hat and bade farewell to his host and hostess.

"But, father, the display has not yet begun," they protested. But he courteously thanked them for their hospitality and departed, walking over the green grass toward a clump of trees about a mile distant.

His host and hostess, who had noticed him talking to the angels, though of course they could not understand what was being said, nor could they discern with whom he conversed, thought him very peculiar.

"They say he is very holy," said the woman looking after him.

"No doubt," said her husband.

Imaginus walked under the bright sun, conversing with Prudentia of the Way of Ultimate Perfection, a subject much given to his mind.

"It is said of Saint Zifferus," said Imaginus, "that having mortified his flesh to the limits of life itself, he refused a glimpse of the Seventh Heaven such as was vouchsafed to Saint Paul. This he did from motives of humility, but suffered instead the sin of ingratitude."

"A difficult decision," remarked Prudentia, lifting a stone out of his way.

"But one that would be offered only to a soul already far gone along the road to perfection," said Imaginus.

"True," agreed Prudentia. She helped him to climb a barbed wire fence and, spreading her wings, sat down beside him on the grass.

For some time they sat in silence, Prudentia watching the aeroplanes with their crowd of attendant angels flying above the field, thankful that Imaginus had not yet taken to aviation. The saint was deep in prayer for the soul of the young man whose plane was even then soaring high into the heavens. Suddenly it could be seen to break away from the others and fling itself in a slanting dive towards the earth. For a moment it straightened out and then came on again with a roar, to crash into the clump of trees under which Imaginus and Prudentia were sitting. The saint had risen as though he knew what was about to happen and was hurrying to the spot. The aeroplane was nose-deep in the earth, surrounded by crushed foliage and boughs from the tree into which it had fallen. Flames were already mounting the wreckage. Imaginus plunged into the fire and lifted the aviator from his seat. The young man was barely conscious and Zestia was flying backwards and forwards through the smoke, crying, "I couldn't help it, I couldn't help it."

Imaginus and Prudentia carried the young man away from the fire and laid him on the soft turf. He opened his eyes and saw the gentle face of the priest beside him. Tears came into his eyes. "Oh, father," he said, "I am so glad you are here." Then he made his confession and composed his soul for death.

A motor-car came bringing a doctor and members of his family. And they took him away accompanied by Zestia, whose raiment had become as radiant as the sun, and a great company of heavenly spirits rejoicing in his conversion.

"It is sad that so young a man should die," said Prudentia who was of rather a sentimental nature.

"He will not die yet," said Imaginus. "He has only broken a collar bone. But I must pray to his patron saint and get him to give Zestia more help."

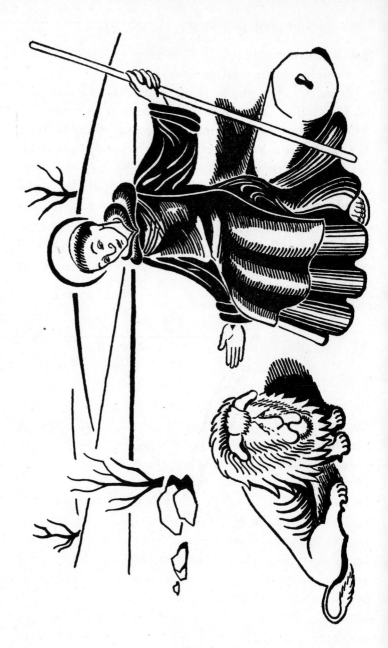

14

3. THE STORY OF THE LION OF JEROME

Saint Imaginus had many adventures and the tales told of him are without number. Like the Holy Man of Assisi, to whom he had a loving devotion, he made friends with all the animals, seeing in them evidences of the Divine Wisdom and the means of increasing grace in his own soul. Legend has it that he was born at Orroroo in South Australia by a miracle, but this is more likely to be true of his survival than of his birth. The following is but one of the many stories told of his concern for animals.

While Saint Imaginus was yet a young man he served as curator or junior priest in the parish of Wog-Wog, in the desert beyond Port Augusta. For in those days the monks of Saint Simplicitas had a house in the desert there and served many parishes in the surrounding country.

Imaginus had at last, by dint of great patience both of his own and of his superiors, brought himself to be worthy of ordination. Shortly afterwards he was ordered to journey across the desert that he might enter on the duties of his ministry. He therefore took the buggy belonging to the Monastery and two lean horses and, placing in the vehicle the bag containing his toothbrush, nightshirt, breviary and rosary beads, and a holy relic of Saint Anselm (his sole worldly possessions saving the clothes he wore) he journeyed for two days

15

and two nights to Wog-Wog, to the house of the Parish Priest who was also a monk of his Order.

In this town did Imaginus live for many years, carrying out his priestly duties with great labour and zeal, to the wonder and astonishment of all who saw him.

Now it is told that on one occasion as Imaginus was crossing the gum creek which at this time of the year was dry (as at all other times of the year except February of each fifth year when there was rain on the Queensland border), he was climbing the steep bank with much exertion and thinking with delight of the tea which would be awaiting him at the presbytery house on his return. As he reached the top of the bank and sat down on a fallen log of sheeoak to rest, a lion approached him. This astonished the saint, as he could not recall ever before having observed lions in Australia. He did not take time to dwell on his astonishment, however, for his compassion was at once aroused by the forlorn and sorrowful appearance of the beast.

"Ah, selfish and ungrateful that I am!" lamented the good monk. "I look forward with delight to the ample tea which will be awaiting me at the presbytery house, while here is a fellow creature famished and in need of help. Come, my poor lion, we will go on together, and as soon as I am able I will provide you with a good meal."

So saying, he went forward at an increased pace, the beast following closely at his heels; and, as he walked, Imaginus revolved in his mind all that he had heard or read concerning lions. After profound cogitation he came to the conclusion that these animals were not native to the country and were but rarely seen in

16

this part of the world. This caused him some perplexity, for, thought he, how did this lion come to be here, so far from civilization? Unless, indeed, it was the Evil One, come to place some singular temptation in his path? At this he stopped and turned to gaze at the lion. But he could find nothing but sorrow and benevolence in the beast's countenance, so that he was forced to conclude that it had no evil intent.

"Why, then," thought he, "it is perhaps a messenger of God." And it struck him that the lion might indeed be the holy Saint Jerome in disguise, come to guard him from some as yet unseen danger. With a heart filled with gratitude to God, Who neglects not even the humblest and least worthy of His servants, Imaginus fell upon his knees in the dust of the roadside and offered up a prayer of thanksgiving.

At Wog-Wog the Parish Priest was having tea and, the day being hot, the door of the house stood open. When the Priest saw Imaginus and his companion coming towards the house, he dropped the cake which he was about to put into his mouth and jumped on the mantelpiece. Imaginus picked up the cake and gave it to the lion.

"Do not be afraid, father," he said. "This poor animal means no harm. He is only hungry and anxious for something to eat."

"Chase him away!" shouted the Priest. "Chase him away and shut the door."

"Why, no, father," replied the saint gently. "I cannot do that, for it is my opinion that this lion is none other than the holy Saint Jerome come to guard us from danger."

"May the holy Saint Jerome guard us indeed!" exclaimed the terrified cleric. "Father Imaginus, I command you to chase the animal away and to close the door."

This Imaginus was therefore forced to do in obedience to the Priest who was his Superior: but not before he had gathered up what food remained and given it to the lion. He then helped the Parish Priest to get down from the mantelpiece for he was rather corpulent and found it difficult to retreat at leisure from a position he had occupied in haste. They then drank their tea, though without food, as the lion had eaten it all.

"Where did you find this lion?" asked the Parish Priest. Imaginus told him, adding his conviction that the beast was Saint Jerome in disguise.

"Nonsense!" exclaimed his Superior. "It probably belongs to the circus which came into the town today."

Toward sunset Imaginus went out into the town to see the circus of which the Priest had told him. It was a poor affair of tent and waggon, with a few dejected animals and a hurdy-gurdy. As the saint neared the place where the circus was, he heard an uproar and commotion and found a number of people shouting and running in different directions. He pressed forward in order to see what caused this confusion and then saw that a man was standing in a corner of a building, hemmed in by the angle of the walls and the presence of the lion, which was crouching menacingly before him. The beast no longer had that benign expression which had so charmed the saint, but was growling and striking with its paws in a manner at once ferocious and terrifying. It was apparent that at any moment it would spring upon and rend its victim.

"What," exclaimed Imaginus. "Is this my friend whom I fed? Is this gratitude, which even beasts should observe in deference to the Creator Who gave them life?" He put his hand on the mane of the enraged animal and continued to chide it in his gentle voice. "Do you not remember the lion of Saint Jerome, my friend, who repaid with obedience and service the kindness of that holy man? We should none of us forget the example of the saints nor cease to emulate those who served them." So saying, he led the lion on one side, the animal following him with docility and lying at his feet as if to show its repentance and submission. It then suffered itself to be led to its cage.

On returning to the presbytery the saint found that the Parish Priest had heard of the incident. "So this is the lion of Saint Jerome!" exclaimed the Priest. "Let me hear no more of this foolishness, Father Imaginus. This will be a lesson to you to give over the absurd inventions you so often practise."

Our saint took this rebuke with silent humility, remembering the example of the lion's submission. A few minutes later the man whom the lion had threatened came to the door and asked for permission to speak to Father Imaginus. He was in great distress, his eyes cast down and his tongue faltering.

"Father, you have saved my life," he said. "For I have starved and ill-treated my lion in order to make him seem savage. He would have killed me. Now let me confess my sins and receive absolution at your hands. For it is many years since I have heard Mass, and you who saved my life must save also my soul." And the man wept.

The saint was moved to pity and heard his confession and asked his name.

"My name is Jerome," said the circus keeper.

"Ah, then it was not I but your patron who saved you," said Imaginus. But because of his humility he said nothing of all this to the Parish Priest, thinking it might become the occasion of pride in his own soul.

4. THE STORY OF THE BISHOP'S PIE

At a time not long after Imaginus met the lion, when he was still serving in the parish of Wog-Wog, it came about that the Bishop of the diocese sent word that on a certain day he would visit that place to bestow the Sacrament of Confirmation on the catechumens who had been prepared by the spiritual labours of the Parish Priest and his assistant, Imaginus.

Now it is well known that the visit of a Bishop is an occasion of great rejoicing, and the Abbot of the Monastery sent word to all the monks serving in parishes that fitting hospitality should be got ready for the Bishop's coming, and the rules of abstinence be somewhat relaxed that no courtesy might seem lacking to the event. For he remembered the teaching of the Abbot Cassian that fasting is useful but love the fulness of the law: the discipline of the flesh but enriching generosity to others in whom we receive, as it were, the Person of Christ.

It is told of this same Abbot of Saint Aegrid's, that, crossing the desert, his horse was overcome with thirst, and the Abbot, seeing him suffer, gave him all the water he had, "for," he said, "this horse also is a creature of God and deserving of life, but I by my sins have forfeited all claim to God's mercy except as may come to me by the merits of Christ."

The following day when the sun was high he sank down and was like to die of thirst, but the horse remembering his goodness lifted him up and brought

21

him safely to a well in the desert. Here they found water in abundance. The Abbot recited six psalms of thanksgiving and filled the water-bags, after which they went on their way.

Now the Parish Priest receiving the Abbot's instructions cast about in his mind for a suitable dish to offer the Bishop for dinner, and having himself a partiality for a pie made with slices of seasoned mutton garnished with kidneys and baked under a thick crust, he ordered a large one to be made in readiness for the Bishop's arrival. This was done and the pie placed on the table.

It so happened and befell that a vagrant passing that way knocked at the door of the presbytery to ask for alms. Imaginus answered the door and was struck by the man's plight and listened with pity to his tale of woe. Finding nought in his pocket with which to succour him, he took the pie off the table and said, "Take this, my poor fellow, it will provide you with food for several days, but neglect not to thank God by Whose providence it comes to be at hand." So saying he gave the pie to the man who went away. The vagrant, who indeed suffered not from hunger but from thirst, took the pie and gave it to the publican in exchange for a flask of wine which, having drunk, he went on his way.

The publican set the pie on his counter where he could admire it (for it was a fine pie) and refresh his appetite by allowing his thoughts to dwell on the eating of it. But presently being called away to attend the affairs of his business, he left his wife in charge who (knowing nothing of the pie nor of how it came to be where it was) sold it to a travelling salesman in exchange for a pair of stockings and a necklace of turquoise.

It was not long after that the Parish Priest, returning to the presbytery, discovered the loss of the pie and inquired of Imaginus its whereabouts. Who told him all that had befallen.

"Blockhead!" cried the Priest and he upbraided Imaginus for his too-ready generosity.

"But, indeed, Father," said Imaginus, "the man was in need."

"I tell you, he is a scoundrel, well known and proved," said the Parish Priest.

"It is true, I gave him the pie not for his merit but for his wretchedness," said the saint sorrowfully.

"What now can we give the Bishop for dinner?" cried the Priest. "Perhaps it is not too late to retrieve the pie." And he ran out of the house.

He found the vagrant already some distance from the town who told him what he had done with it, and the Priest hied him back to the hostelry where he inquired of the publican if he could return the pie. This the publican agreed to do, but only if the priest would pay for the bottle of wine which the vagrant had received in exchange for it. The Priest gave him the money and the Publican (thinking that his wife had taken the pie to the kitchen) went to fetch it, but quickly found that his wife had dispensed with it. Nothing remained for the Priest to do but to search for the travelling salesman who had taken the pie, and this he did, finding him at last sitting under a gum tree eating peanuts.

"Will you give me back the pie?" asked the Parish Priest.

"Gladly," said the travelling salesman, "but first you must pay me the price of the stockings and the turquoise necklace I gave the publican's wife in exchange for it."

The Priest gave him the money and they went to the lodging of the travelling salesman to fetch the pie. Here they found that the landlady of the travelling salesman had locked up the pie in her kitchen and refused to part with it until the travelling salesman had paid the rent he owed her. This he refused to do, for the money the Priest had given him was not enough to discharge his obligation to the woman. So the Priest paid the woman what was owing, and taking the pie with gladness, he returned to the presbytery.

He told Father Imaginus all that had happened.

"How wonderful are the ways of God!" exclaimed Imaginus. This pie has provided refreshment to the poor vagrant, objects of use and pleasure to the publican's wife, money to the travelling salesman who sorely needed it, and rent to the woman to whom it was owed."

The arrival of the Bishop prevented the Parish Priest from replying. Greetings were given and they sat down to dinner.

The Bishop rubbed his hands with pleasure and remarked on the fine appearance of the pie which indeed had suffered no hurt from its travels and adventures. At that moment there came a loud knocking at the door. Imaginus answered it and found there a poor woman who pleaded for help, saying with piteous moans that she had nothing wherewith to feed her family of eight children.

The Bishop asking to know the reason of the interruption, was touched with pity by her plight.

"Alas, that any should suffer want!" he exclaimed with tenderness, and picking up the pie, carried it to the door.

"Here, my poor soul," he said, "this will suffice to feed your children for several days, but do not neglect to thank God by Whose Providence it comes to be at hand." So saying he gave the pie to the woman who went away.

"Indeed, my lord," protested the Parish Priest, "what will we now have for dinner?"

"Better a dish of herbs where love is," said the Bishop, "than a dinner of pie while others are in need." He then said Grace and helped himself to bread of which there was abundance.

5. THE STORY OF HOW IMAGINUS WAS REBUKED BY A DOG

One day Imaginus was digging in the Monastery garden, when he uncovered a worm who lived there. He picked it up and placed it on the bank that it might be safe from the spade; but the worm was discontented and upbraided him for his carelessness. Whereupon a blackbird who was perched nearby swooped down and swallowed the worm at one gulp.

Now Imaginus, who had accepted the worm's reproaches with meekness, found his meekness changing to anger, and he in turn rebuked the blackbird.

"How many times," he said, "have I not rescued you from Felicitas (the Monastery cat), who would have eaten you as you have swallowed this poor worm? This is ingratitude for which you should repent."

But the blackbird only sang loudly, persuading herself that she had saved Imaginus from an impudent enemy, but, in truth, enjoying the sensation of well-being bestowed on her by the worm.

Felicitas and Monitor (the Monastery dog) were sitting not far away, listening to all that had taken place, and Felicitas, angry that the blackbird had scorned the admonition of the holy monk, prepared to spring upon her and frighten her into repentance. Imaginus seeing her intention, forbade her, saying, "How sad I am that you too, Felicitas, should desire the blood of a fellow-creature. Have you not promised me many times, in return for the porridge and milk I give you

27

every day, to refrain from killing the birds and small beasts who live in the Monastery garden? Now do I see how grievous was the sin of Adam which cast the lust for evil even over the innocent beings of God's creation. Henceforth I forbid you to kill even for food, under penalty of being expelled from the garden, as Adam was expelled from Paradise."

At these words a silence fell on all the garden.

At last Monitor roused himself and spoke. "Doubtless what you say is true, good father, that it was by the sin of Adam that we fell from innocence. Yet, that being accomplished, who can compel a man to be good? If abstinence from blood be good then let us accept it, not by compulsion but voluntarily, as a means of bringing us nearer Paradise. For, as it was by a movement of his own will that Adam turned away from God, should it not be by an act of our own will that we return to Him?"

"There is wisdom in your words, Monitor," said Imaginus.

The dog laid his head against the monk's knee. "Is it not true, my father, that men sometimes sacrifice themselves for each other? Is it not then permissible for the birds and beasts of the earth to serve each other by death as well as by life? In this is the meaning of Love, which is service for God's sake. Yet should this sacrifice be a gift and not demanded by force."

Felicitas, hearing these words, drew in her claws and said to the blackbird, "Monitor is right. Go in peace, Cantatrice. I will eat my porridge." And the blackbird, with her head on one side, said, "It will not be said that I was less generous than a cat," and she

cast up the worm and laid it at Imaginus's feet. Then she ate two berries off a nearby bush, but they were bitter.

Then said Imaginus to Monitor, "How came you to be so wise, my friend?"

And Monitor laid him down and licked the straps of the monk's sandals and replied, "I have been the servant of many men."

A brother coming into the garden and seeing Imaginus as he thought idle, reproached him and told him to pursue his work.

"Indeed, brother," replied the saint, "this idleness has not been without profit, for I have learnt much concerning the first virtue, which is charity."

"It remains necessary, nevertheless," said Monitor, getting up, "to observe the first duty, which is obedience."

6. THE STORY OF THE INCONVENIENT HARVEST

There came a time when Imaginus was sent from the Abbey of Saint Aegrid (which is in the desert) to a small house in the city where several brethren of his Order lived in community according to the Rule of Saint Simplicitas and ministered to the needs of the people who dwelt thereabouts. It is said that Imaginus stayed there for a year, singing daily the Divine Office and labouring among the poor of whom there were a great many in that place.

By now, so great had Imaginus grown in sanctity that he dwelt entirely in the spirit of the Lord, subduing his flesh by fasting and discipline and pouring out his soul in vigils. Thus it was that, strengthened by the overmastering Grace of God, he was able to work many miracles, healing the sick and in other ways bringing about numerous wondrous happenings.

One day, while he was praying in the chapel of the Monastery his soul was caught up to Heaven and ravished by Divine Love so that he no longer saw or felt the things of earth. But after some time, returning to himself a little, he understood how God had given to men the means of sustaining life: the fruits of the earth for the sustenance of their bodies, the knowledge of truth for the quickening of their minds, and the Holy Sacramental Bread for the continual refreshment of their souls. And Imaginus cried out, imploring God on behalf of those among whom he worked, for he was

31

stricken at their poverty and wretchedness which knew
not the very necessities of spiritual and bodily comfort.
And God spoke to him so that he went away renewed
in faith.

Coming to the shop of a baker who lived near the
Monastery, he said to him, "Friend, you see how many
people in this city have not the wherewithal to buy

THE INCONVENIENT HARVEST

your loaves, so that they are starved and weak from lack of nourishment. Can you not give them the bread they need and so earn for yourself the blessing of God?"

The baker, listening, spoke gently (for he was a good Christian man): "Indeed, father, I give so much and so much of my bread to the poor, and I can do no more, for the necessity of making some small profit on which to keep myself and my family. But why do you not speak to the miller, for it is the high price I must pay for my flour that prevents me from asking less for my bread."

So Imaginus betook himself to the miller and spoke to him in the same way. Who replied angrily, thinking it to be some trick to deprive him of his profits, "for," said he, "how can I lower the price of my flour when the farmers charge so much for the wheat? Let that rascally baker look to his own doings. I have no mind to put money into his pocket." In vain did Imaginus urge upon him the needs of the poor. He merely cried out the louder of his own needs and those of his family, so that Imaginus was obliged to go away unsatisfied.

After that he went into a country district where there were many farmers and he spoke to them of the matter; and some listened with patience and others with indifference, but all in agreement that they could not sell their wheat at a lower price because of the high cost of dispatching it to market.

Then Imaginus began to understand that it is the burdens men themselves impose upon the produce of

33

the earth which render it inaccessible to so many of their fellows.

Returning to the city he remained far into the night rapt in thought and prayer. It seemed to him at last that if the harvest of the fields could be brought to the doors of those who needed bread, much of their necessity would be relieved.

Now it must be understood that Imaginus was endowed with the gift of working miracles, and this must explain how, on the following morning, the streets of the city were found to be thickly covered with a fine crop of wheat in full ear, ripe and ready for the reaping. Nothing could surpass the astonishment of the citizens when they saw the roads and sidewalks filled with the harvest, or their anger when motor cars and bicycles were unable to penetrate its growth. And failing in their pride to see in this miraculous abundance a symbol of the bread they had withheld from their poorer brethren, they ordered it to be gathered up and burnt because of its impediment to their daily pursuit of wealth. "For," cried the bakers and the millers, "if corn is now so plentiful how can we sell our flour and bread at a high price? And if we cannot sell our flour and bread at a high price, how can we provide for our families?"

But the more they destroyed the harvest, the faster it grew, so that men scarce dared to open their doors for fear the wheat would thrust its way within. Moreover, the grain falling in heaps upon the ground, filled the gutters and overflowed into the basements of the buildings where it sprouted afresh. Neither man nor beast, nor any vehicle, could move about the city for the density of this miraculous harvest.

But the poor rejoiced, for they found that they had only to pluck a little of the corn for it to become the finest and whitest flour, and there was no hunger among those people for many days. But the other citizens had no contentment in this simple fare, and their anger turned against God, Whom they reproached for His judgments on them.

Imaginus, hearing and seeing these things, wept and was ashamed for the sinfulness of the world and the pride and folly of men, and only the knowledge of his own sins and his great love for God preserved him from despair.

Now when he saw what had befallen, the Prior of the Monastery rebuked Imaginus for his stupidity and presumption. "Look you, Father Imaginus," he said, "at the distress and inconvenience which have been caused by this untimely occurrence. For His own purposes God has granted you the ability to do such things, but the power to work miracles, like all His gifts, should be used with prudence and restraint. It is better that our work in the world be done by ordinary means, with patience and long-suffering."

Imaginus took these words to heart, and gave himself up to a life of increased obedience and penance. But the Lord Abbot, who had been present when the Prior reproached Imaginus, spoke no word, for he saw in the soul of Imaginus a great charity. And dwelling in his own mind on the Infinite Wisdom of the Most High, the Abbot understood that God sometimes punishes worldly men, not by deprivation and misfortune, but by heaping upon them an abundance of material goods so that their minds are distracted with riches and know neither peace nor satisfaction. And going to Imaginus, the Abbot asked him to hear his confession.

7. THE STORY OF THE OBSTINATE COW

Many and wonderful are the tales told of Saint Imaginus, for men do not cease to recall the benevolence of this holy man. Among other events of his long and fruitful life may be told the story of the obstinate cow.

Upon a certain day Imaginus was walking along a country road, when he heard sounds of rage and lamentation coming from a neighbouring field. Hastening through the hedgerow, he went to enquire the cause of the disturbance and found there a man shouting and cursing at a cow, while at the same time he belaboured her with the milking stool which he held in his hand.

No one could have been more amazed at this sight than Imaginus, for he was accustomed to see the accord with which the farmers and their beasts served one another in his countryside. On being asked the reason for his anger, the farmer explained that in spite of the best of food and the kindest of treatment the cow refused to give her milk. At last the farmer had lost all patience with her obstinacy and would fain be rid of her, "for," said he, "she is nothing but a burden, eating up good pastures and giving nothing in return."

Imaginus, seeing that the cow was but a cause for anger in the man, offered to take her away, and, the farmer willingly agreeing, he picked up the halter and led her out of the field.

Once on the highroad, Imaginus was sorely perplexed as to what to do with the cow, for he had no experience of these animals and knew very little of what was expected of him in the matter. Nor could he hope for any assistance from the cow in an affair so contrary to her liking.

At last he bethought him of some holy nuns who had a house not far off and who might grant asylum to the beast for the time being. Moreover, the example of their modesty and the gentle discipline of conventual life might have a salutary effect on one of so wayward a temper. So thither Imaginus made his way.

Now, when the people of the nearby town (which is called Kapunda) saw their Parish Priest approaching with the cow, they all ran out of their houses and uttered exclamations of astonishment, for they could not remember ever having seen such a sight before. Many of them followed him to the convent (which is on the top of a high hill) and, the day being warm, Imaginus found it difficult to maintain the customary serenity of his demeanour. The cow, moreover, did not give herself willingly to be led. By the time they reached the convent gate, a great crowd had gathered, and some of the townsfolk were laughing at what seemed to them a comical spectacle.

One fellow, bolder than the rest, openly made fun of the good Priest, till the cow, who had by no means participated in these events with any good grace, no sooner heard him mocking Imaginus than (such was the perversity of the beast) she threw down her horns and gored the ruffian into a briar bush, whence Imaginus had perforce to rescue him, not without some hurt to

39

himself. The cow, in the meantime, cantered into the convent grounds.

The nuns (who in this place are of the Order of Saint Dominic) gladly welcomed the cow and promised Imaginus that they would give her every care. And so it befell. They gave her into the charge of the youngest and gentlest of their number, a novice named Hyacinth.

Every morning at dawn Hyacinth led the cow (whom she called Benevolentia) into a field where she fed all day on buttercups and sweet grass. At evening, about the hour of the Angelus, she was shut into a little byre where the evening sun had warmed the stones, and there she remained for the night.

Hyacinth and Benevolentia came to love each other very much, and the little novice often confided to the cow the small perplexities of her daily life in the convent, begging Benevolentia to teach her the secret of patience and benignity. She also related to her the lives of the saints so that each might hold before the other the example of perfection. Especially did she love to tell the stories of Saint Kevin and the other saints of Ireland: of how Saint Malo cherished a little wren, and Saint Kevin won the affection of a cow who drew such sustenance merely from his sanctity that the richness and abundance of her milk became famous throughout the country. To these stories and many others did Benevolentia listen with great amiability, but she still refused to give her milk, for her love was not yet greater than her pride.

Now at this convent there also lived a cat. He had no name but the nuns called him Ishmael, from his habit of roaming out of doors. Each day, after Hyacinth had led Benevolentia to her field, Ishmael would come and try to persuade her to yield some milk; but each day the cow refused, saying that she had no mind to give what was her own to those who had no claim on it. "A need is always a claim," persisted Ishmael. "Not for those for whom greed is always a name," retorted Benevolentia, making a play on the words.

And so the days passed, and Ishmael had not succeeded, either by cajolery or sophistry, in making the cow give her milk. At last the cat resorted to cunning and, coming to the byre early one morning before the sun was up, he told the cow that the nuns had decided to send her to the butcher to be killed as they could no longer afford to keep in idleness one who was so unprofitable.

At these words the cow was greatly afraid, and her fear was not lessened when Hyacinth came to lead her out into the field, for the novice was weeping and the cow could not fail to believe that her approaching death was the cause of this sorrow. The truth was that the novice had been told that she was to be sent to another convent and she wept at thus being parted from her friend.

"My sweet Benevolentia," she exclaimed, "we must accept this parting with resignation if not with cheerfulness. Earthly affection must not stand in the way of our duty, for we know that there remains no happiness for us except in service to others for God's sake." And so saying she embraced the cow with tenderness and went away.

It will be seen that these words in no way comforted Benevolentia who was more convinced than ever that her death was at hand. Moreover (let it be said), she too was sad at the prospect of being separated from so gentle a mistress. She therefore spoke to the cat when he came to see her in the evening and told him to tell those he met that Benevolentia had plenty of milk for all who needed it. From that time she gave two full buckets of milk each day, of which Ishmael had a generous share.

When Saint Imaginus heard of this he rejoiced and came with haste to the convent, praising the cow that she had at last come to the practice of generosity and virtue. And finding an almond tree blooming by the wayside, he plucked some branches of the blossoms and hung them round her neck. And the nuns too made much of her and showed her such affection as to make the cow full of compunction for her former obstinacy and pride.

Not long after these events which we have related, Imaginus met Ishmael the cat, and as soon as he saw him he perceived the wrong that Ishmael had done. And he reproached him with it. But Ishmael would not repent. "By my little tale," he said, "I have brought Benevolentia to a better way of life. Is this not worthily done?"

"It is never permissible to do wrong for a good purpose," replied Imaginus.

"Yet it is agreed," said the cat, "that repentance may be sought through fear of punishment no less than through hope of reward. Is this not so, my father?"

"It is so," said Imaginus. "None the less, you have lied to Benevolentia, and must do penance. For three days you will abstain from milk, and on the fourth day you will tell her of your sin and ask her forgiveness."

The cat rubbed itself against the monk's habit and purred, for he knew that the cow would rejoice to hear that she was not after all to be sent to the butcher.

After that they all lived happily together, and the little novice came often from the other convent to see her friend.

8. THE STORY OF THE ASTONISHED
STOCKBROKER

It happened that Imaginus was serving in a certain
parish when the Bishop of the place called all the
priests together to discuss in what way they could build
a new hospice for the poor, of whom there were very
many in great need. It seemed that in order to build
the hospice the sum of twenty-two thousand pounds
would be needed, and neither the Bishop nor any of
his priests knew where to obtain so large an amount
of money.

For a long time they debated how this might be done,
but Imaginus sat in silence, praying that God would
show them some means of helping His poor.

At last one of the priests suggested that a certain
wealthy stockbroker be asked to give some of the money.
"He is reputed to be a man of good heart," he said.

"Yes, but also a man of worldly intent," said another.
"I doubt whether the cause of religion would appeal
to his generosity."

"Nevertheless, he is very wealthy," said a third.

Imaginus went out from the assemblage and made his
way to the office of the stockbroker, who was greatly
astonished as he had never before seen a monk of the
Order of Saint Simplicitas, much less received one in
his office.

"Well, good father," said he, "what do you want?"

"Twenty-two thousand pounds," said Imaginus.

45

"Indeed," said the stockbroker, "how do you propose to get so large a sum?"

"I thought perhaps you would give it to me, as you are very rich," said the monk.

Then the stockbroker was more astonished than ever, and exclaimed, "But I have not so much money in the world."

Imaginus, thinking that he protested because of the hardness of his heart, began to tell him of the poor people whom the Bishop wished to help, and of how the blessing of God would surely be poured out on anyone who could help so gracious a work. The stockbroker listened patiently (for he was not a bad-hearted man) and when Imaginus was finished said to him: "Father, no doubt had I been able I would have given you some money for this work; but the truth is that I am poor myself," and he went on to explain that his ventures had failed and, not only had he no money for his own needs, but he was without means of paying his debts.

At this Imaginus was much cast down, not merely with sympathy for a human being in such distress, but because he saw that injustice would be done to others if the man's debts were not paid. With many expressions of comfort, he therefore took his departure.

As he walked down the street he met one of his parishioners (for the monks of Saint Simplicitas were serving parishes in that place) who asked him: "Why are you so cast-down, good father?" To which Imaginus replied, "On behalf of a friend, who lacks the means of paying his just debts." Then the parishioner (though he was a poor man) gave Imaginus a shilling and went his way. But he told many others of Imaginus's sadness, and such was the love they bore him that people came from far and near to give him a little money. And though their gifts were small, so great was their love and so large their number that after a time Imaginus found that their offerings amounted to a hundred pounds, which he showed to his Superior, the Parish Priest, who was very pleased and praised Imaginus for his diligence in the matter.

Then Imaginus came again to the stockbroker and gave him the money, who could not contain his amazement. "How did you come to have so much money, who so recently came to me with nothing?" he asked. "It is not my money," explained the good man, "but has been given by many friends, each a little from his poverty, that they might help you in your need."

Not many days after this the Parish Priest enquired of Imaginus the whereabouts of the money. "I have given it to the stockbroker," he said. The Parish Priest could not conceal his chagrin. "Your foolishness surpasses everything, Father Imaginus," he cried. "This money was meant to help in the building of the hospice for the poor, and you thoughtlessly give it away to a man who is wealthy and without a single worldly need unsatisfied."

Imaginus accepted this rebuke with meekness but felt the need of defending the stockbroker. So he explained that the man had lost all his money and had none wherewith to pay his debts. But the Parish Priest would not listen to anything in his defence and sent Imaginus to ask for the return of the money.

Imaginus came once more to the office of the stockbroker whom he found in a jovial mood. With trembling voice Imaginus explained how he had been bidden to ask the return of the hundred pounds.

"What!" exclaimed the stockbroker. "Did you not intend it as a gift?"

"Indeed, yes," replied Imaginus in distress, "but it seems that I was mistaken in thinking myself free to dispose of the money in the way I wished."

"Well," said the stockbroker, "this time you there will be no such mistakes. Here is the hundred you gave me, and here is a second hundred for yourself, as a mark of my gratitude to those who helped me in my time of need," and so saying he pushed the money across the table to Imaginus. It was now the monk's turn to be astonished, and he asked how the stockbroker came to possess so large a sum. "Truly," said he, as he gathered up the money, "to those who cast their bread upon the waters shall it be returned an hundredfold."

"Not bread, father, not bread," replied the stockbroker, "just the bulls and the bears, just the bulls and the bears," and he laughed heartily. "And that is not all. I have now over thirty thousand pounds."

"Thirty thousand pounds!" exclaimed Imaginus, jumping up from his seat. "Thirty thousand pounds! Then you will be able to give me the twenty-two thousand pounds which is needed for building the hospice for the poor, besides having more than enough for the settlement of your debts. Thank God for His infinite mercies," and he began to chant a Te Deum.

When at last Imaginus said "Amen," the stockbroker began to count money into a bag which he gave to Imaginus. "Here it is," he said, "twenty-two thousand pounds. Pray for me, father."

Imaginus took up the bag and went back.

When Imaginus arrived at the presbytery the Parish Priest was having his dinner. "Well, father," he said, "Did you get the money?"

"Yes," replied Imaginus.

"That is well," said the Priest. "And let this be a lesson to you, not to take on yourself the presumption of imprudent generosity." And so saying he picked up the bag. In doing so of course he noticed its weight. "What is this?" he exclaimed. "There seems here to be more than one hundred pounds. How much is there?"

"Twenty-two thousand pounds," said Imaginus.

"But where did you obtain twenty-two thousand pounds?" demanded the Parish Priest.

"From the stockbroker," replied the monk. "By his bravery in facing many wild beasts he has obtained more than enough for his needs, and has given this sum to God's poor."

Greatly excited, the Parish Priest took up the bag and (having finished his dinner) hurried away to the Bishop. But Imaginus went into the church to pray for the soul of the astonished stockbroker.

9. THE STORY OF THE OBEDIENT PIGEONS

It might be thought that Imaginus grew rich by the wonders he performed. But rather the contrary. The fruits of the world are gathered by him who values the world; but Imaginus laboured only for God and was so rewarded.

It thus came about that the Church of the brethren of St. Simplicitas fell into decay and they had not the means of repairing the ravages which time had wrought: the stones of the porch broken and worn, the plaster peeling from the walls. Moreover, a crevice appeared in the roof so large that the devotions of the brethren were disturbed by the rain which dripped upon them, and the chanting of the Divine Office was interrupted by the chattering of the birds as they flew in and out. The parishioners were not lacking in goodwill but they were thriftless and lazy and not given to exerting themselves for anything other than their own profit.

At last the Prior spoke of his vexation to Imaginus, who replied, "I cannot deny the justice of your complaint, Father Prior, but were it not better to take these shortcomings to ourselves? Are we not men? Has God not given us the means whereby we may labour as other men? In this holy state of religion to which He has called us we may be perfected by the work of our hands no less than by the aspirations of our hearts." And the Prior agreed.

Imaginus said further, "I know where there is a

hammer. Let us go, therefore, and mend the roof of the church." And they went out together.

Coming to the church they went in and, having given thanks to God, they set about the task on which they had resolved.

Now the ladder that they had was as too short and could in no wise be made to reach to the place in the roof where the hole was. But setting it against the wall Imaginus ascended to the top of the archway. "Do you mount also, Father Prior," he said, "and when we are both on the summit of this archway you can take me up on your shoulders and in this way we can reach the hole; for I am spare of body and no great weight."

And the Prior, whose habit of austerity was not apparent in the strength of his frame, mounting the ladder took Imaginus up on his shoulders. And Imaginus saw the hole in the roof and it was much larger than he had as first supposed.

"I fear this will take much mending, Father Prior," he said.

"Then do you make haste," said the Prior. "You may be spare of body but your boots do not spare my shoulders."

The sky can be seen through this hole," said Imaginus.

"Then be quick and close it," said the Prior, "for I cannot hold you much longer."

"It is undoubtedly a matter for some skill," said Imaginus.

"Then be at it," said the Prior, "for the mud on the hem of your habit has already blinded me."

"The pigeons are flying in and out," said Imaginus.

"Will you hurry!" said the Prior. "My back is like to break under your weight."

"These pigeons belong to the blacksmith," said Imaginus. "I have seen them on the roof of the smithy." And he continued to talk to the pigeons while striving to replace the timbers of the roof.

"Father Imaginus," cried the Prior. "Will you give over this foolish talking and set about the work before I am exhausted." Whereupon he made an impatient movement with his feet which caught the top of the ladder and threw it to the ground.

"Now here is calamity," exclaimed the Prior. "How are we to get down from the top of this archway without the ladder?"

"Be of good heart, Father Prior," said Imaginus. "I have no doubt that God has caused us to be in this predicament for some good purpose."

"That well may be," said his Superior. "Doubtless for our sins. Nevertheless, your weight does not decrease. Pray apply yourself to the means by which you may come down."

But Imaginus seemed not to hear and continued to talk, as it were, to himself.

"Father Imaginus, to whom are you talking that you heed so little my entreaties?" asked the Prior.

"Indeed, Father Prior," replied Imaginus, "I hear what you say and I have your sufferings at heart. Even now I am telling the pigeons of them."

At this the Prior quite lost his patience and gave way to wrath.

"Selfish and stupid Imaginus!" he cried. "Is it possible that while I groan beneath your weight you have nought better to do than to prate with the birds? Send them away, I command you, and come down from there. Exercise some care besides, or you are like to bring us down more quickly than we came up."

Imaginus spoke to the pigeons and bade them fly away. Which they did. He then gave his attention to the descent, but neither by venture nor by care could he find a way of coming down from his position on the Prior's shoulders without the risk of precipitating them both from the top of the archway.

Then did the Prior with lamentations begin to bewail their lot for that they could neither go up nor come down except in danger of injury; moreover, as time went on, they would grow faint with hunger and would swoon to the ground.

Imaginus sought to comfort him and exhorted him to have faith. "Do you not remember the prophet Elijah," he said, "whom the ravens fed and whom Providence preserved even in the desert? Is it likely that Heaven in whose service we have been brought to such a pass will leave us without succour? Indeed it is certain that we will soon be released for I have told the pigeons to go quickly for help."

"Oh, what wickedness is this," groaned the Prior, "that at such a time you have no thought but of frivolous speaking and vain imaginings. It were better to prepare for death." And he began to recite the Confiteor.

In the meantime, the pigeons had flown to their home on the roof of the smithy, and there by the beating of their wings and loud croaking in the ears of the smith had so awakened his curiosity as to the cause of their strange behaviour that he fetched a number of his neighbours and followed the pigeons in their flight back to the church. When they saw their pastors in such a plight all was confusion and perplexity; but at last ropes were brought that Imaginus might descend in safety from the shoulders of the Prior, and the ladder was set up again that both might come down.

Then did the parishioners ask many questions about this remarkable occurrence. And Imaginus told the company all that had befallen, and he spoke of the Prior's great strength and of his courage during this trial and of how but for his endurance Imaginus would have fallen and been killed. Then the parishioners were ashamed of their laziness and worked with great zeal to restore the church. But the Prior said nothing.

10. THE STORY OF THE INDIGNANT VIOLET

At one time, before Imaginus was sent away from the Monastery of St. Aegrid to work in a parish, a certain brother complained to him of the dullness of his conversation; "for," said he, "I have never heard you speak of the glories of religion, nor refer to those exercises of the soul in its search for perfection which should surely occupy the mind of one who has given himself to the life of contemplation."

And Imaginus told him of Zachary, the disciple of Silvanus, who, being asked what he saw of divine mysteries, replied, "Naught better than to hold one's peace." Whereupon the brother sought to lead Imaginus to further counsel, but he would not, and went his way in silence.

On another occasion, while walking in the Monastery garden, a brother besought Imaginus to instruct him in the virtue of humility. And Imaginus said to him, "Behold this violet which grows here in the garden bed. It hides its head under the leaves, yet its perfume is shed for the enjoyment of all those who come near. This tall sunflower with its bright flower can be seen from afar, but has no perfume with which to enrich its glory. We should strive to be like the hidden violet rather than the sunflower, that our virtues being secret, may sweeten all the house. Therein lies humility."

When the brother, much edified, had departed, the violet raised her head and cried out to Imaginus for

what he had spoken concerning her. "It is not of my own will that I am lowly and hidden," she said, "but by the forcefulness of this upstarting sunflower, who has smothered me with his great leaves and cast me into the shadow. It is an injustice against which I have no redress."

Imaginus, greatly astonished, turned to the sunflower and asked him of the matter; who answered in a gentle voice, "Indeed, good father, by my growth I have thrust this poor violet aside, and can compensate but poorly for depriving her of sun by protecting her from storm and wind. Nor can I prevent my petals from assuming the bright colour they acquire after the buds are open. It is by God's will that I have attained to such a stature, and in thanksgiving to Him Who made me, I must turn my face to Heaven."

Then was Imaginus overcome with shame at his own presumption in judging others by appearances, for he perceived in the sunflower the true humility which accepts the Will of God with holy joy. Hurrying after the departed brother he cast himself at his feet and begged his forgiveness, "for," said he, "in presuming to instruct you I have offended against the very virtue I sought to teach." The brother, marvelling at his wisdom, raised him up and embraced him and together they went into the church, praising God.

But the violet, when she saw that Imaginus could so abase himself, was ashamed at her own complaint, and she wept. The sunflower looked tenderly down and sought to cheer her, saying, "You heard how the holy man praised the beauty of your perfume. Now rejoice that God has blessed you by thus enabling you to serve with sweetness the whole garden." And the violet was comforted and wept no more.

11. THE STORY OF THE UNGRATEFUL BRICKLAYER

It has been told how Imaginus was gifted with the power to work miracles, and how, on divers occasions, he brought about wondrous happenings to the edification of the multitude and the consternation of his Superiors. So much was this the case, that at last he was forbidden to work miracles, except by permission of the Abbot or the Prior of the Monastery where he lived.

Imaginus was in no wise cast down, for he had every confidence in the wisdom of those set in authority over him and he longed only to perfect his soul by the practice of a happy obedience. He asked permission to help those who were sweeping the city streets of the grain which he had caused by his miraculous power to grow along the pavements. This the Abbot granted him.

For many days Imaginus laboured and it may be thought that he sometimes regretted having brought about such an abundant harvest. This was not so. He saw only evidence of the power of God which had brought the corn into being and his labour he offered in thanksgiving.

One day while he was thus engaged he met a grasshopper. The little creature jumped through the air and alighted at the monk's feet.

"See how far I can fly," he boasted. "There is no one who has such strong legs and such fine beautiful wings."

Imaginus tried to teach him the value of humility,

pointing out that his strength was due in no wise to any merit of his own, but was wholly dependent on the bounty of God. But the grasshopper would not agree and continued to praise himself and his accomplishments.

Imaginus saw that he would not learn in the pride of life, but he prayed that in misfortune more wisdom might come to him. "Remember," he said to the grasshopper, "if ever you are overcome with weakness and cannot fly, repent of your vanity and call upon God that His finger may sustain you."

The grasshopper gaily promised (for he was a cheerful fellow) and he hopped beside Imaginus as he set out on his return journey to the Monastery. Their way lay along the city streets where many people were moving to and fro. After a time the grasshopper found it convenient to hide in the folds of the monk's habit, for fear of being walked on by the passers-by. But he said nothing of this to Imaginus as he was ashamed that his fine jumping did not safeguard him from the traffic.

They had gone some distance when they came to a high building, on the top of which, some workmen were laying bricks. The building was so tall that from below the bricklayers looked no larger than the grasshopper himself.

As Imaginus and Chirripus (for that was the grasshopper's name) walked past the building, one of the bricklayers missed his footing and began to fall through the air towards the earth. "This man," said Chirripus to himself, "can fly through the air much further than I can," and he lost a little of his vanity.

The people in the street also watched the man and

began to cry out loudly and to run together into a crowd. Seeing them point upwards with their fingers, Imaginus raised his head from the reverie into which he had fallen. When he saw the man rapidly approaching from above, he was overcome with dismay, for he realised that the man would be killed if he hit the ground. It was, however, not so much the bricklayer's death which concerned the good monk, as the fact that, if he should be killed, his soul would undoubtedly be lost for ever.

Never had Imaginus felt himself in such a dilemma. He longed to beg the mercy of God to save the man's life; but he would rather have died himself than commit the sin of disobedience by performing a miracle. It would be necessary then to obtain the permission of his Superiors. Crying loudly to the bricklayer to await his return, he gathered up the skirts of his habit and made off to the Monastery with all speed.

At the Monastery the Prior was instructing a class of catechumens in the merits of the Nine First Fridays. He sustained Imaginus's interruption with patience and received his request with equanimity.

"Were I to grant you permission to do as you desire," he said, "the time is already past for it to be of profit, for by now the poor man has fallen to the ground. May God have mercy on his soul."

"Amen," said Imaginus. "But indeed it is not as you think, Father Prior. For I dared not commit the sin of disobedience by working a miracle without your permission, so I bade the man wait for my return and came with all haste to the Monastery."

"What!" exclaimed the Prior, jumping to his feet.

"Do I understand that you have left the man in mid-air?"

"That is undoubtedly the case," said Imaginus. Whereupon the Prior ran out of the house, followed by Imaginus and all the catechumens.

When they came to the place where the bricklayer was they found a large crowd of people. Some firemen were raising ladders.

Imaginus looked at the bricklayer and felt very sad, for he saw that the man's soul was dark with sin, and he longed to bring him to repentance.

"Have I your permission, Father Prior," he said, "to save the life of this poor fellow?"

"Yes, yes," said the Prior. "Bring him down."

Imaginus raised his hand. Very gently and slowly the bricklayer came to earth. Imaginus put his hand on the man's shoulder. "How grateful you should be," he said, "to the Infinite Mercy of God Which has thus saved you from death."

But the man, in a rage at being, as he thought, made to look a fool before so many people, would have struck Imaginus had he not been constrained by two policemen and a chartered accountant.

Now Chirripus, who had remained hidden in the folds of Imaginus's habit, had seen and heard all that had taken place. Becoming incensed at the bricklayer's ingratitude he hopped across and bit him sharply on the ankle. He then accompanied Imaginus and the Prior and all the catechumens back to the Monastery.

After a time the bricklayer found that his foot became red and swollen. Finding it easier to suffer repentance for his sins than the pain of his wound, he repaired to the Monastery to seek the aid of Father Imaginus. There he met the Prior and had perforce to listen to much good counsel concerning the state of his soul and the necessity of leading a Christian life. Then the Prior gave him absolution and a poultice for his foot and sent him away.

Imaginus, who in silence had seen all this, spoke to the grasshopper with loving benevolence. "Well done, little Chirripus," he said. "What I sought to do by extravagant means you have accomplished by lowly ones." But the grasshopper who had learnt his lesson would not accept the praise.

"Hold out your finger, Father Imaginus," he said. "I am weary of flying."

12. THE STORY OF IMAGINUS AND THE HEAVENLY FLOWERS

While Imaginus was serving in a certain parish the Parish Priest was wont to remonstrate with him on his habit of falling into an ecstasy during the offering of the Mass. "The people of this place have many occupations and much press of business," said the Parish Priest. "If they leave the Church before the *Initium sancti evangelii* they commit grievous sin; yet you, by your dalliance in contemplation, keep them from their affairs and there is confusion and complaint."

Such was the humility of Imaginus that he desired not even his devotions to be vexatious to others; and he promised that in future he would watch himself lest he again fall into an abstraction during the Holy Sacrifice.

It chanced about this time that Imaginus was called by telephone to attend a sick person in a distant part of the town. Hurrying there to carry out the duties of his ministry, Imaginus came at last to a dark and squalid house where he enquired the whereabouts of the sick person. What was his dismay to find a company of people who greeted him with ribaldry and who made game of him, pointing to a woman of lewd countenance who laughed and jested in a way which caused Imaginus to close his ears with shame. Then he saw that there was indeed no sick person and that he was made the subject of an evil jest. Turning about he made his way

back to the presbytery where he told the Parish Priest all that had happened.

And with his heart weighed down with sorrow Imaginus did great penance in reparation to God for the wickedness of men.

Not long after this Imaginus was again called to attend a sick person in the same neighbourhood and made preparations to go, but the Parish Priest forbade him, saying that such people should not be encouraged to indulge their evil ways. "But, father," said Imaginus, "how do we know that this time one of their number is not really ill and in need of spiritual succour lest he die in his sins?"

"Father Imaginus," replied the Parish Priest "you are young and ill instructed in the wickedness of the world. Do you not see that these people are but the instruments of the devil, bringing you to such a house that they may spread evil reports concerning you? To sully your good name and give support to those who would attribute the lowest vices to the servants of God? I cannot permit you to go lest you in your weakness be tempted to some folly. But that there may be no mistake I will go myself and see."

So the Parish Priest went and to him happened all that Imaginus had experienced, but that the ruffians did laugh the louder at the priests for having fallen victims a second time to their plotting. Then was the Parish Priest enraged and returning he forbade Imaginus to go near the house again. And Imaginus wept and increased the austerity of his penances.

Some time later the same thing happened again, but the Parish Priest would not permit Imaginus to go to the house. Imaginus instantly implored him, "for," said he, "it may well be that now someone is really dying and they may be brought to repent their sins before the moment of death." But the Parish Priest would not relent and Imaginus had perforce to obey him. And he spent the night in prayer imploring God's mercy on those who had so abused him, and beseeching heaven to grant to them the grace of a Christian death.

Now it so befell that the next day was the Feast of the Immaculate Conception of the Blessed Virgin; and many people came to the church to attend Mass.

While he was offering the Holy Sacrifice Imaginus found his thoughts turning towards the Mother of Christ with a tender reverence, and as he contemplated the shining purity of her person he saw that indeed the Parish Priest had been right in judging him a weak and sinful man. And he cast himself down before the altar and begged the intercession of the Immaculate Mother for his soul and the souls of all sinners. And straightway he was caught up into the glory of heaven in an ecstasy of adoration so that he lost all count of time and the place wherein he was.

When the poeple had waited a long time they began to lose patience and to murmur among themselves; and one bolder than the rest went into the presbytery and told the Parish Priest who, coming, waked Imaginus out of his contemplation and brought him to the conclusion of the Mass. And when they had made their thanksgiving and left the church the Parish Priest spoke sharply to Imaginus and rebuked him for his lack of obedience and said to him, "Do you know, Father

Imaginus, that this is a very busy district? We have not enough priests to attend to all the demands of the parish. There are the sick to attend, the school to visit, the catechumens to instruct, the boys to teach; tonight there is a meeting of the parish committee, this afternoon a meeting of the football club, and tomorrow the annual general meeting of the mothers' circle. Besides there is the monthly magazine to print and the bazaar and ball to organize. You cannot expect me to undertake all this without your help. I must therefore insist that you spend less time in dreaming and pay more attention to your daily duties." And Imaginus saw the justice of the Parish Priest's complaint and readily gave his promise.

The Parish Priest returned to the presbytery, but chancing to glance out of the window a few minutes later he saw to his chagrin that Imaginus was kneeling among the grasses of the churchyard wrapped in prayer. Then did the Parish Priest become very angry and threw up his hands in despair. "What will our parishioners think?" he exclaimed to himself. "If they see one of their priests kneeling in the churchyard we will be brought into ridicule." And going out he called to Imaginus to rebuke him severely.

Imaginus hearing the Parish Priest's voice break in on his meditations rose obediently and went to receive his instructions. Whereupon the Parish Priest saw that in the grass where Imaginus had been kneeling was a ring of snow-white flowers as though an angel had knelt there. Then was the Parish Priest struck silent; and he took Imaginus's hand in his and said to him, "My son, forgive me," and going into the church he remained for a while. Presently taking the Sacred Species from the tabernacle he hid It under his cloak and went out into the street to the house of the evil woman whom he found at the point of death. And he heard her confession and absolved her. And the perfume from the heavenly flowers filled the whole house.

And from that time he rebuked Imaginus no more.